I am a **FOTONOVEL.** Someone went to a movie, and wants to tell you <u>everything</u> about it, re-viewing it in its most visible moments. I'm only a book, so I can't quite set the pictures in motion, but I can do one thing a movie can't: I can tell you what the stars were thinking, or what they might have thought.

I am a **FOTONOVEL,** where all media converge, the newsiest novelty since the novel, and the comeliest since the comix. I speak all tongues and can tell all tales — in color!

I am a **FOTONOVEL,** the ultimate re-run. I'm the film at your fingertips, in a room alone with the stars; I'm the moment that passes in the twinkling of an eye, engraved in your memory, <u>forever</u>...

D0926020

HERE's
GREASE!

A MAJOR PARAMOUNT PICTURE
Starring

JOHN   OLIVIA
TRAVOLTA and NEWTON-JOHN

Producers
ROBERT STIGWOOD   ALLAN CARR

Director
RANDAL KLEISER

GREASE ™

A
FOTONOVEL PUBLICATIONS
FOTONOVEL ™

Based on the screenplay by
BRONTE WOODARD

Adaptation by
ALLAN CARR

Based on the original musical by
JIM JACOBS and WARREN CASEY

Original Fotonarration by
MICHAEL NEWMAN

Cover and interior design by
MICHAEL PARISH

Graphic devices by
THOMAS WARKENTIN

GREASE

Published by
Fotonovel Publications
8031 Sunset Boulevard
Los Angeles, CA 90069

GREASE FOTONOVEL
Copyright © 1978 by Paramount Pictures Corporation.

ISBN: 0-89752-000-9
Printed in the United States of America.
Published simultaneously in the United States and Canada.
First Fotonovel Publications Printing — June 1978

Oh
Sweet
Summer
Lovin'...

GREASE

STARRING

JOHN TRAVOLTA
AS DANNY ZUKO

OLIVIA NEWTON-JOHN
AS SANDY

STOCKARD CHANNING
AS RIZZO

JEFF CONAWAY
AS KENICKIE

THE **FIRST** DAY OF SCHOOL!

YES, IT'S DANNY ZUKO, HOOD OF HOODS, ALREADY MAKING TIME.

SUMMER NIGHTS

Danny: SUMMER LOVIN'! HAD ME A BLAST.
   MET A GIRL CRAZY FOR ME.
Sandy: SUMMER LOVIN'! HAPPENED SO FAST.
   MET A BOY CUTE AS CAN BE.
Both: SUMMER DAY, DRIFTING AWAY,
   TO UH-OH, THOSE SUMMER NIGHTS.

Thunderbirds: OH WELL. TELL ME MORE, TELL ME MORE.
   DIDJA GET VERY FAR?
Pink Ladies: TELL ME MORE, TELL ME MORE.
   LIKE, DOES HE HAVE A CAR?

Danny: SHE SWAM BY ME; SHE GOT A CRAMP.
Sandy: HE RAN BY ME, GOT MY SUIT DAMP.
Danny: SAVED HER LIFE. SHE NEARLY DROWNED.
Sandy: HE SHOWED OFF SPLASHING AROUND.
Both: SUMMER SUN, SOMETHING BEGUN,
   THEN UH-OH THOSE SUMMER NIGHTS!

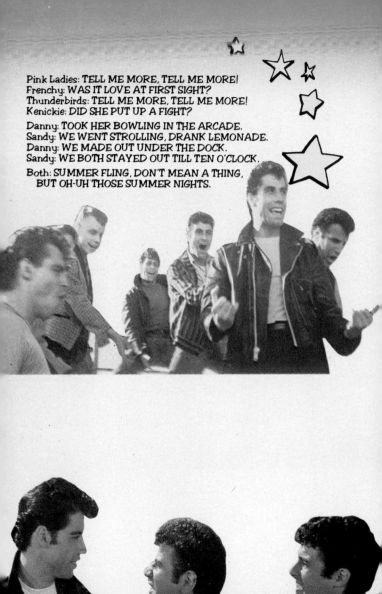

Pink Ladies: TELL ME MORE, TELL ME MORE!
Frenchy: WAS IT LOVE AT FIRST SIGHT?
Thunderbirds: TELL ME MORE, TELL ME MORE!
Kenickie: DID SHE PUT UP A FIGHT?

Danny: TOOK HER BOWLING IN THE ARCADE.
Sandy: WE WENT STROLLING, DRANK LEMONADE.
Danny: WE MADE OUT UNDER THE DOCK.
Sandy: WE BOTH STAYED OUT TILL TEN O'CLOCK.

Both: SUMMER FLING, DON'T MEAN A THING,
   BUT OH-UH THOSE SUMMER NIGHTS.

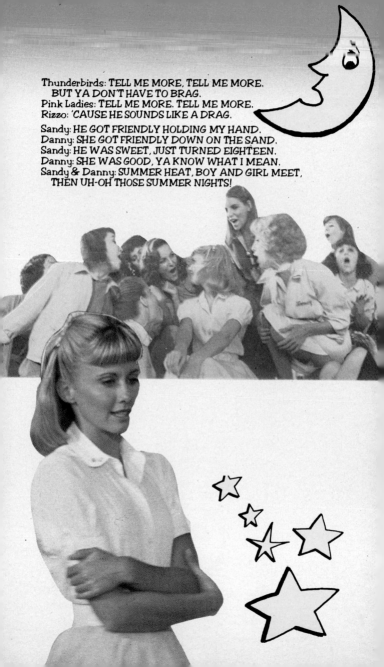

Thunderbirds: TELL ME MORE, TELL ME MORE.
 BUT YA DON'T HAVE TO BRAG.
Pink Ladies: TELL ME MORE. TELL ME MORE.
Rizzo: 'CAUSE HE SOUNDS LIKE A DRAG.

Sandy: HE GOT FRIENDLY HOLDING MY HAND.
Danny: SHE GOT FRIENDLY DOWN ON THE SAND.
Sandy: HE WAS SWEET, JUST TURNED EIGHTEEN.
Danny: SHE WAS GOOD, YA KNOW WHAT I MEAN.
Sandy & Danny: SUMMER HEAT, BOY AND GIRL MEET,
 THEN UH-OH THOSE SUMMER NIGHTS!

Sandy: IT TURNED COLDER, THAT'S WHERE IT ENDS.
Danny: SO I TOLD HER WE'D STILL BE FRIENDS.
Sandy: THEN WE MADE OUR TRUE LOVE VOW.
Danny: WONDER WHAT SHE'S DOING NOW.

Both: SUMMER DREAMS, RIPPED AT THE SEAMS,
BUT UH-OH! THOSE SUMMER NIGHTS.
Thunderbirds: TELL ME MORE, TELL ME MORE.

MUMP!! MRUMP!!

If they do we'll be ready.

LOOK AT ME, I'M SANDRA DEE!!

LOOK AT ME, I'M SANDRA DEE
LOUSY WITH VIRGINITY
WON'T GO TO BED TILL I'M LEGALLY WED.
I CAN'T, I'M SANDRA DEE.
WATCH IT, HEY, I'M DORIS DAY
I WAS NOT BROUGHT UP THAT WAY
WON'T COME ACROSS, EVEN ROCK HUDSON LOST
HIS HEART TO DORIS DAY.

I DON'T DRINK UNDWEAR
I DON'T RAT MY HAIR
I GET ILL FROM ONE CIGARETTE
KEEP YOUR FILTHY PAWS OFF MY SILKY DRAWERS
WOULD YOU PULL THAT STUFF WITH ANNETTE?

AS FOR YOU, TROY DONAHUE
I KNOW WHAT YOU WANNA DO
YOU GOT YOUR CRUST, I'M NO OBJECT OF LUST
I'M JUST PLAIN SANDRA DEE.
ELVIS, ELVIS, LET ME BE
KEEP THAT PELVIS FAR FROM ME

JUST KEEP YOUR COOL
NOW YOU'RE STARTING TO DROOL
EH! FONGOOL!!
I'M SANDRA DEE.

HOPELESSLY DEVOTED TO YOU

GUESS MINE IS NOT
THE FIRST HEART BROKEN
  MY EYES ARE NOT THE FIRST TO CRY
I'M NOT THE FIRST TO KNOW
  THERE'S JUST NO GETTING OVER YOU.

YOU KNOW I AM JUST
A FOOL WHO'S WILLING
  TO SIT AROUND AND WAIT FOR YOU.
BABE CAN'T YOU SEE
THERE'S NOTHING ELSE FOR ME TO DO,
  I'M HOPELESSLY DEVOTED TO YOU.

YOU PUSHED MY LOVE ASIDE,
  I NODDED MY HEAD,
HOPELESSLY DEVOTED TO YOU,
  HOPELESSLY DEVOTED TO YOU,
  HOPELESSLY DEVOTED TO YOU.
MY HEAD IS SAYING
FOOL, FORGET HIM.
MY HEART IS SAYING DON'T LET GO
  HOLD ON TO THE END
AND THAT'S WHAT I INTEND TO DO,
  I'M HOPELESSLY DEVOTED TO YOU.

BUT NOW THERE'S NOWHERE TO HIDE
  SINCE YOU PUSHED MY LOVE ASIDE,
I NODDED MY HEAD,
  HOPELESSLY DEVOTED TO YOU,
  HOPELESSLY DEVOTED TO YOU,
  HOPELESSLY DEVOTED TO YOU.

GREASED LIGHTNIN'

WE'LL GET SOME OVERHEAD LIFTERS
  AND FOUR-BARREL QUADS, OH, YEAH
A FUEL-INJECTION CUT-OFF
  AND CHROME-PLATED RODS, OH, YEAH
WE'LL GET IT READY —I'LL KILL TO GET IT READY.

WITH A FOUR-SPEED ON THE FLOOR.
  THEY'LL BE WAITIN' AT THE DOOR
YOU KNOW THAT AIN'T NO SHIT
  WE'LL BE GETTIN' LOTSA TIT
IN GREASED LIGHTNIN' —GO GO GO

GO, GREASED LIGHTNIN'
YOU'RE BURNIN' UP THE QUARTER MILE
GREASED LIGHTNIN' GO GREASED LIGHTNIN'
YEAH, GREASED LIGHTNIN'
YOU'RE COASTIN' THROUGH THE HEAT-LAP TRIALS
GREASED LIGHTNIN', YEAH GREASED LIGHTNIN'

YOU ARE SUPREME
THE CHICK'LL CREAM
FOR GREASED LIGHTNIN'!
WE'LL GET SOME PURPLE FRENCH TAIL-LIGHTS
AND THIRTY-INCH FINS, OH YEAH
A PALOMINO DASHBOARD
AND DUAL MUFFLER TWINS, OH YEAH
WITH NEW PISTONS, PLUGS, AND SHOCKS,
YOU CAN GET OFF YOUR ROCKS
YA KNOW THAT I AIN'T BRAGGIN',
SHE'S A REAL PUSSY WAGON.
GREASED LIGHTNIN'!

GO, GREASED LIGHTNIN'
YOU'RE BURNIN' UP THE QUARTER MILE
GREASED LIGHTNIN', GO GREASED LIGHTNIN'
YEAH, GREASED LIGHTNIN',
YOU'RE COASTIN' THROUGH THE HEAT-LAP TRIALS
GREASED LIGHTNIN',
YEAH, GREASED LIGHTNIN'
YOU ARE SUPREME
THE CHICKS'LL CREAM
FOR GREASED LIGHTNIN'!

YOU ARE SUPREME
  UH-HUH
THE CHICKS'LL CREAM
  UH-HUH
FOR GREASED LIGHTNING
  GO GO GO

I'LL HAVE ME PURPLE FRENCH
  TAIL LIGHTS AND THIRTY-INCH
  FINS, OH YEAH
A PALOMINO DASHBOARD
  DUAL MUFFLER TWINS, OH YEAH
WITH NEW PISTON PLUGS
  AND SHOCKS I CAN GET OFF
YOU KNOW I AIN'T BRAGGIN'
  SHE'S A REAL PUSSY WAGON
SHE'S GREASED LIGHTNIN'

GO GREASED LIGHTNING,
YOU'RE BURNIN' UP THE QUARTER MILE
  GREASED LIGHTNIN' GO GREASED LIGHTNIN'
GO GREASED LIGHTNIN'
YOU'RE COASTIN' THROUGH THE HEAT-LAP TRIAL
  GREASED LIGHTNIN', GO GREASED LIGHTNIN'

YOU ARE SUPREME
  UH-HUH
THE CHICK'LL CREAM
  UH-HUH
FOR GREASED LIGHTNIN'
GO GREASED LIGHTNING
  YOU'RE BURNING UP THE QUARTER MILE
GREASED LIGHTNIN' GO GREASED LIGHTNIN'
GO GREASED LIGHTNING
  YOU'RE COASTIN' THROUGH THE HEAT-LAP TRIAL
GO GREASED LIGHTNIN' GO GREASED LIGHTNIN'

Well, if you find him, give him my phone number.

YOUR STORY'S SAD TO TELL
    A TEENAGE NE'ER DO-WELL
MOST MIXED-UP NON-DELINQUENT ON THE BLOCK
    YOUR FUTURE'S SO UNCLEAR NOW WHAT'S LEFT OF YOUR CAREER NOW?
CAN'T EVEN GET A TRADE-IN ON YOUR SMOCK—

WHO KEEP THE FEEBLE HOPES ALIVE?
WHAT ARE YOU PROVIN'   WHAT ARE YOU PROVIN?
YOU GOT THE DREAM BUT NOT THE DRIVE

IF YOU GO FOR YOUR DIPLOMA YOU
COULD JOIN A STENO POOL
TURN IN YOUR TEASING COMB
AND GO BACK TO HIGH SCHOOL
BEAUTY SCHOOL DROPOUT   BEAUTY SCHOOL DROPOUT
HANGIN' AROUND THE CORNER STORE
BEAUTY SCHOOL DROPOUT
                                        BEAUTY SCHOOL DROPOUT
IT IS ABOUT TIME YOU KNEW THE SCORE
WELL, THEY COULDN'T TEACH YOU
                    OOH
ANYTHING   OOH
ANYTHING   OOH

YOU THINK YOU'RE SUCH A LOOKER

OOH

BUT NO CUSTOMER WOULD GO TO YOU
UNLESS SHE WAS A HOOKER
BABY DON'T SWEAT IT   DON'T SWEAT IT
YOU'RE NOT CUT OUT TO HOLD A JOB
BETTER FORGET IT   FORGET IT
WHO WANTS TO HAVE THEIR HAIR DONE BY A SLOB?

NOW YOUR BANGS ARE CURLED,

OOH

YOUR LASHES TWIRLED,

BUT STILL THE WORLD IS CRUEL

OOH

WIPE OFF THAT ANGEL FACE AND GO
BACK TO HIGH SCHOOL

OOH

SANDY AND DANNY DANCE UP A STORM.

AND WINS ACCLAIM.

There they are, ladies and gents. The new champs. Could I have your names please?

Cha Cha Di Gregorio and Danny Zuko!

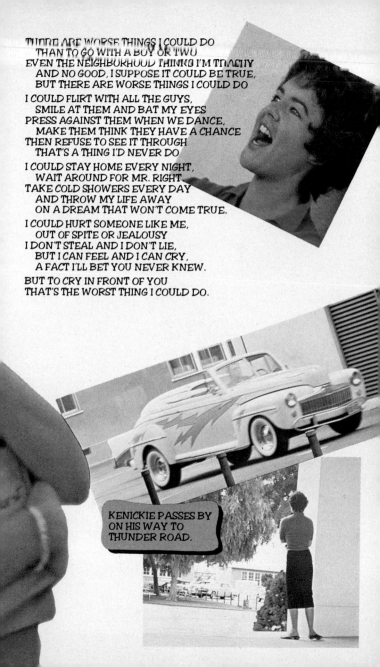

THERE ARE WORSE THINGS I COULD DO
    THAN TO GO WITH A BOY OR TWO
EVEN THE NEIGHBORHOOD THINKS I'M TRASHY
    AND NO GOOD, I SUPPOSE IT COULD BE TRUE,
    BUT THERE ARE WORSE THINGS I COULD DO

I COULD FLIRT WITH ALL THE GUYS,
    SMILE AT THEM AND BAT MY EYES
PRESS AGAINST THEM WHEN WE DANCE,
    MAKE THEM THINK THEY HAVE A CHANCE
THEN REFUSE TO SEE IT THROUGH
    THAT'S A THING I'D NEVER DO

I COULD STAY HOME EVERY NIGHT,
    WAIT AROUND FOR MR. RIGHT.
TAKE COLD SHOWERS EVERY DAY
    AND THROW MY LIFE AWAY
    ON A DREAM THAT WON'T COME TRUE.

I COULD HURT SOMEONE LIKE ME,
    OUT OF SPITE OR JEALOUSY
I DON'T STEAL AND I DON'T LIE,
    BUT I CAN FEEL AND I CAN CRY,
    A FACT I'LL BET YOU NEVER KNEW.

BUT TO CRY IN FRONT OF YOU
THAT'S THE WORST THING I COULD DO.

KENICKIE PASSES BY
ON HIS WAY TO
THUNDER ROAD.

THE LAST DAY OF SCHOOL !!

Attention, Seniors. Before the merriment of commencement commences, I hope that your years with us here at Rydell have prepared you for the challenges you face. Who knows? Among you there may be a future...

Eleanor Roosevelt.

Rosemary Clooney.

...or even a Doris Day.

SPLATT!!

THE TEACHER

25¢

ALL IN THE SPIRIT OF A GOOD CAUSE!

YOU'RE THE ONE THAT I WANT
   YOU OO OO HONEY THE ONE THAT I WANT
YOU OO OO HONEY THE ONE THAT I WANT
   YOU OO HONEY
THE ONE THAT I WANT YOU OO OO
   ARE WHAT I NEED — YES IN-DEED — YES IN-DEED

IF YOU'RE YOU'RE THE ONE THAT I WANT
   YOU OO OO HONEY THE ONE THAT I WANT
YOU OO OO HONEY THE ONE THAT I WANT
   YOU OO OO ARE WHAT I NEED — YES IN-DEED

IF YOU'RE FILLED — WITH AFFECTION
   YOU'RE TOO SHY TO CONVEY
BETTER TAKE MY DIRECTION
   FEEL YOUR WAY

I BETTER SHAPE UP 'CAUSE YOU NEED A MAN
   (I NEED A MAN) WHO CAN KEEP — ME SAT-IS-FIED
I BETTER SHAPE UP — IF I'M GON-NA PROVE (YOU BETTER PROVE)
   THAT MY FAITH IS JUSTIFIED
'CAUSE I'M SURE NOW I'M SURE DOWN DEEP INSIDE

YOU'RE THE ONE THAT I WANT YOU OO OO HONEY
   THE ONE THAT I WANT YOU — OO OO HONEY
THE ONE THAT I WANT YOU OO OO ARE WHAT I NEED — YES IN-DEED
   IF YOU'RE YOU'RE THE ONE THAT I WANT YOU OO OO HONEY
THE ONE THAT I WANT — YOU OO OO HONEY
   THE ONE THAT I WANT — YOU OO OO
ARE WHAT I NEED — YES IN-DEED

WE GO TOGETHER

WE GO TOGETHER
  LIKE RA MA LA MA LA MA KA DING-ITY DING-DE DONG
REMEMBER FOREVER
  AS SHOO BOP SHA WA DA WADIE YIPITY BOOM DE BOOM
  CHANG CHANG CHANG-ITY CHANG SHOO BOP
THAT'S THE WAY IT SHOULD BE
  WAH OOH YEAH!

WE'RE ONE OF A KIND
  LIKE DIP DA DIP DA DIP DOO WOP A DOO-BY DOO
OUR NAMES ARE SIGNED
  BOGEDY BOGEDY BOGEDY SHOO-BY DA WOP
  CHANG CHANG CHANG-ITY CHANG SHOO BOP
WE'LL ALWAYS BE LIKE ONE
  WAH WAH WAH WAH AH

WHEN WE GO OUT AT NIGHT
  AMD STARS ARE SHINING BRIGHT
UP IN THE SKIES ABOVE
  OR AT THE HIGH SCHOOL DANCE
WHERE YOU CAN FIND ROMANCE
  MAYBE IT MIGHT BE LOVE
WHERE YOU CAN FIND ROMANCE
  MAYBE IT MIGHT BE LA-A-A-AH-OVE!

WE'RE FOR EACH OTHER,
  LIKE A WOP BABA LU MOP
JUST LIKE MY BROTHER
  SHA NA NA YIPPITY DIP
  CHANG CHANG-A CHANGITTY
WE'LL ALWAYS BE TOGETHER!

FULL CIRCLE.
FROM SUMMER TO SUMMER
WITHOUT LOSING THAT
SWEET SUMMER LOVE. AND
WHAT NEXT? ANOTHER
SUMMER OF GREASE? OR
THE DRY LOOK? WAIT'LL
NEXT YEAR!

A HAPPY ENDING!!